A Map of Your State

Use the map of the United States on page R10 of your social studies textbook to make a map of your own state.

Copy or trace the shape of your state onto a sheet of paper. Locate and label your state capital. Then add a compass rose. Color your map and give it a title. The title of your map could be the name of your state.

McGraw-Hill School Division

Mystery State in the Northwest

Look at the map of the United States on page R10 of your social studies textbook. Use these clues to find the mystery state:

> The northeastern border of this state touches Montana and Canada. The capital of this state is about 450 miles east of the Pacific Ocean.

Write the name of the mystery state on a sheet of paper. Then make up two clues for your own mystery state. Be sure to use direction words in your clues.

McGraw-Hill School Division

A Trip to Nashville

Look at the map of the United States on page R10 of your social studies textbook.

Suppose you and your family want to take a trip from your state capital to Nashville, Tennessee. Which states would you pass through along the way? List the states in order on a sheet of paper. Next to each state write the name of its capital.

McGraw-Hill School Division

Find the Cities

Use the map of the United States on page R10 of your social studies textbook to find the following cities:

- **Reno, Nevada**
- **Springfield, Illinois**
- **New Orleans, Louisiana**

List the cities on a sheet of paper. Next to each city write the numbers of the lines of latitude and longitude that are closest to that city.

McGraw-Hill School Division

A Young Nation

Which Country?

Use the world map on page R16 of your social studies textbook to find the mystery country. Here are the clues:

I am a country located in both Europe and Asia. I border the Arctic Ocean to the north. Which country am I?

A Young Nation

Mystery City

Use the maps of the United States on pages R10 and
R12 of your social studies textbook to find the mystery
city. Here are the clues:

> This city is a state capital. It is located near a large
> bay of the Atlantic Ocean. The bay does not border
> New Jersey.

Write the name of the mystery city and the bay on a
sheet of paper.

A Young Nation

Get to Know Alaska

Use the maps of the United States on pages R10 and R12 of your social studies textbook to answer these questions:

- **Which bodies of water border Alaska?**
- **What is the capital of Alaska?**
- **About how many miles from the west coast of Alaska is Mt. McKinley?**

Write the answers to these questions on a sheet of paper.

McGraw-Hill School Division

A Young Nation

The Gulf of Mexico

Suppose you know a scientist who wants to study wildlife near the coast of the Gulf of Mexico. The scientist has asked you which of the United States he will have to visit in order to see all of the coastline near the gulf. Use the map of the United States on page R10 of your social studies textbook to help you figure out which states the scientist must visit. Make a list of the states.

The Mountain Mystery State

Use the map of the United States on page R12 of your social studies textbook to find this mystery state:

This state is almost completely mountainous. It has more than 150 miles of coastline on the Atlantic Ocean.

Write the name of the mystery state on a sheet of paper. Then make up clues for another mystery state. Be sure to include clues about the landforms in the state.

A Young Nation

Latitude and Longitude

Turn to the maps of latitude and longitude on page **G5** of your social studies textbook. Then copy these sentences:

- Lines of latitude measure the distance from the prime meridian.
- Lines of longitude extend north and south.
- Latitude lines extend north and south.

If a sentence states something true, write *T* next to it. If a sentence is false, write *F* next to it. Rewrite each false sentence so it says something true.

Continent Chart

Use the world map on page R16 of your social studies textbook and the hemisphere maps on page G5 to make a chart of facts about the continents. The chart should include:

- the name of each continent
- the hemispheres in which each continent is located

You can organize the information under the headings *Continent* and *Location*.

McGraw-Hill School Division

A Young Nation

Country Detective

Turn to the map of the Western Hemisphere on page R20 of your social studies textbook. Use these clues to find the mystery country:

This country is south of the equator and west of 60°W longitude. Its capital city is Lima.

Write the name of the mystery country on a sheet of paper. Then make up clues for another mystery country. Be sure to include latitude and longitude in your clues.

McGraw-Hill School Division

More Latitude and Longitude

Use the maps of latitude and longitude on page 40 of your social studies textbook to answer these questions:

- In which direction do lines of latitude extend?
- What do lines of latitude measure?
- In which direction do lines of longitude extend?
- Where do lines of longitude begin and end?

Write the answers to these questions as a paragraph about latitude and longitude.

McGraw-Hill School Division

A Young Nation

A Route in South America

Use the map of the Western Hemisphere on page R20 of your social studies textbook to follow these directions:

Find the capital of Venezuela. Travel south from this city until you reach 30°S latitude. Follow 30°S latitude east until you reach the Atlantic Ocean. What city is located there?

Write the name of the city and the country. Then list all the countries you passed through along the way.

McGraw-Hill School Division

Your State: True or False?

Turn to the map of the United States on page R10 of your social studies textbook. Copy these sentences:

- My state is west of the Mississippi River.
- My state is more than 300 miles from the 110°W meridian.
- My state is less than 600 miles from the border of Canada.

If a sentence states something true about your state, write *T* next to it. If a sentence is false, write *F* next to it. Then rewrite each false statement to make it true.

McGraw-Hill School Division

By the Pacific Ocean

Turn to the map of the **Western Hemisphere** on page **R20** of your social studies textbook. Name two North American countries that border the Pacific Ocean and have land west of 90°W longitude.

A Young Nation

Finding Locations

Suppose you know someone who is learning how to make maps. Your friend needs help with a map of the Western Hemisphere. Use the map of the Western Hemisphere on page R20 of your social studies textbook to help you find these locations:

- 60°N latitude, 150°W longitude
- 30°N latitude, 120°W longitude
- 0° latitude, 60°W longitude

Write the name of the city that is located nearest where the lines of latitude and longitude cross.

McGraw-Hill School Division

A Young Nation

Regions

Turn to the map of Regions of the United States on page 29 of your social studies textbook. Then answer the following questions:

- Of which region are Florida and Arkansas a part?
- Which states in the West region border the Southwest region?
- Which region extends farthest east?

Write the answers as sentences in a paragraph about regions of the United States.

Sailing Around the World

Use the world map on page R16 of your social studies textbook to plan a sailing trip around the world. Your trip must begin and end in Hawaii. You may not cross any land.

Write a description of the route you would take. Be sure to name the bodies of water you would cross and the directions in which you would travel.

Map Scale: True or False?

Turn to the maps of Hawaii on page G7 of your social studies textbook. Then copy these sentences:

- The scales on both maps show only miles.
- On both maps the scales show that one inch equals 150 miles.
- On both maps the distance between Niihau and Oahu is about 130 miles.

If a sentence states something true, write *T* next to it. If a sentence is false, write *F* next to it. Then rewrite each false statement to make it true.

From Atlantic to Pacific

Turn to the map on page R10 of your social studies textbook. Suppose you know someone who wants to travel across the United States from the coast of the Atlantic Ocean to the coast of the Pacific Ocean. To make sure she follows a straight route, your friend wants to follow the line of 40°N latitude. Use the map of the 50 United States on pages R14 and R15 to find which states your friend will cross. On a sheet of paper, list the states in order.

McGraw-Hill School Division

Georgia and North Dakota

Use the map of the United States on page R10 of your social studies textbook to complete a chart.

	Georgia	North Dakota
borders an ocean		
is north of 40°N latitude		
is east of 90°W longitude		

Copy the chart onto a sheet of paper. Then put a check in the box next to each phrase that describes Georgia or North Dakota.

Native Americans

Turn to the map of Native Americans in the 1500s on page 76 of your social studies textbook. In which cultural area did the Inuit live? Which other Native Americans lived in the same area?

In which cultural area did the Cheyenne live? Which other cultural areas bordered that area?

Cities Near
40°N Latitude

Turn to the map of the United States on page R10 of
your social studies textbook. Find 40°N latitude. Which
cities are near 40°N latitude? List them on a sheet of
paper in order from west to east.

A Young Nation

In Pennsylvania

Look at the road map of Pennsylvania on page G11 of your social studies textbook. Suppose you wanted to travel from Harrisburg to State College. What route should you follow?

Suppose you wanted to go to Willamsport after State College. Write directions to follow.

McGraw-Hill School Division

River
Riddle

Use the map of the United States on page R12 of your social studies textbook to solve a river riddle.

I flow from the northeast to the southwest. My source is in the Rocky Mountains. I empty into the Gulf of California. Which river am I?

Mountains East and West

Look at the map of the United States on page R12 of your social studies textbook. Find as many mountain ranges as you can. List the names of four ranges on a sheet of paper. Write *west* next to mountain ranges that are west of 90°W longitude. Write *east* next to mountain ranges that are east of 90°W longitude.

McGraw-Hill School Division

East of the Mississippi River

Turn to the physical map of the United States on page R12 of your social studies textbook. Find the part of the United States that is east of the Mississippi River. Write the word *northern* on a sheet of paper. Write the names of three landforms or physical features found in the northern part of the eastern United States.

Mystery States

Look at the map of the United States on page R10 of your social studies textbook. Use this clue to find the mystery states:

These states are crossed by 110°W longitude. Which four states could the mystery state be? Write the names on a sheet of paper. Then write one more clue that would narrow the mystery states from four to one mystery state.

In Which State?

Turn to the map of Latitude and Longitude on page 41 in your social studies textbook. Then answer these questions:

- In which state does 45° N latitude cross 100° W longitude?
- In which state does 35° N latitude cross 80° W longitude?
- In which state does 30° N latitude cross 85° W longitude?

Write the name of each state.

McGraw-Hill School Division

A Young Nation

Your Own Mystery State

Use the map of the United States on page R10 of your social studies textbook to write clues that would help someone else find a mystery state. Choose a state to write about. Then write a sentence for each clue.

- Tell where the state is located.
- Name other states that are nearby.
- Name the state capital.

McGraw-Hill School Division

A Young Nation

Using a Map Key

Look at the map of African Kingdoms on page 121 of your social studies textbook. Which of the following questions could you answer using the map key?

- How did people get from the Mediterranean Sea to Gao?
- Which was farther south—Kilwa or Mombasa?
- When did the Kongo kingdom begin?
- About how far from Zanzibar was Zimbabwe?

Elevation and Relief Maps

Use the maps on page G10 of your social studies textbook to complete a chart.

	elevation	relief
shows changes in Earth's surface		
uses shading to show differences in land height		
shows land height above sea level		

Copy the chart onto a sheet of paper. Put a check in the box next to each phrase that describes the elevation map or the relief map.

McGraw-Hill School Division

A Young Nation

The Voyages of Columbus

Use the map showing the Voyages of Columbus on page 142 of your social studies textbook to finish this paragraph:

On his _____ voyage, Columbus sailed to _____ and met the Taino. Columbus sailed for the second time in _____. Nearly ten years later, Columbus began his _____ voyage. He sailed _____ of Hispaniola and _____, then reached the east coast of _____.

Which State Capital?

Turn to the map of the Southeast on page 33 in your social studies textbook. Find Nashville, Tennessee. Then answer the following questions:

- Which state capital is about 450 miles southeast of Nashville?
- Which state capital is less than 300 miles southeast of Nashville?
- Which state capital is about 450 miles southwest of Atlanta?

Write the answers to these questions as sentences.

McGraw-Hill School Division

A Young Nation

Find the Old City

Suppose you found a journal of an explorer. One entry describes the location of an old city. Look at the map of the world on page R16 of your social studies textbook. Then read the clues and try to figure out where the city is.

The city is east of 20°E longitude. It is near the Tropic of Cancer in a country that borders to the east of what is now Libya.

In which country is the old city? On which continent?

A Young Nation

A Pen Pal in North America

Suppose you received a letter from a pen pal in North America. In the letter the pen pal described his life along the coast of the Pacific Ocean.

Use the map of the Western Hemisphere on page R20 of your social studies textbook to find countries where that pen pal might live. Make a list of the countries.

McGraw-Hill School Division

The Equator

Find South America on the map of the Western Hemisphere on page R20 of your social studies textbook. Then answer these questions:

- Which three countries does the equator cross?
- Which country in South America is north of the equator and west of Guyana?
- Which two countries are entirely between the equator and Tropic of Capricorn?

Write the answers to these questions as sentences.

McGraw-Hill School Division

All Around Florida

Turn to the physical map of the world on page R21 in your social studies textbook. Suppose you were visiting the Florida Peninsula.

- Which body of water is to the west of the Florida Peninsula?
- Which body of water is to the east of the Florida Peninsula?
- Which plains are located to the north and northeast of the Florida Peninsula?

Mountains of North America

Turn to the map of the **Western Hemisphere** on page R21 of your social studies textbook. Then answer the following questions:

- Which mountain range is found in the west of North America?
- In which directions does it extend?
- Which countries does it cross?

Write the answers to these questions as sentences in a paragraph about the mountains of North America.

A Visit to the Southeast

Use the map of the Southeast on page 33 of your social studies textbook to finish this story:

Mrs. Ramos left _____, the capital of Virginia, and drove southwest to Montgomery, the capital of _____. Next she drove about _____ miles to New Orleans. Then she drove about 150 miles _____ to Jackson, Mississippi.

Copy the story onto a sheet of paper. Use a number, a direction word, the name of a state, or the name of a city to complete each sentence.

A Young Nation

A Visit to Mt. Rainier

Turn to the physical map of the United States on page R12 of your social studies textbook. Find Mt. Rainier. Then copy these sentences:

- **Mt. Rainier is the tallest mountain in the United States.**
- **Mt. Rainier is north of Mt. St. Helens.**
- **Mt. Rainier is about 300 miles from Canada.**

If a sentence states something true, write *T* next to it. If a sentence is false, write *F* next to it. Rewrite each false sentence so it says something true.

An Historical Map: True or False?

Turn to the map of the 13 Colonies on page G11 of your social studies textbook. Then copy these sentences:

- The map shows the United States in the 1800s.
- Maine was part of the New Hampshire colony.
- There were two different groups of colonies in the 1800s.

If a sentence states something true about the map, write *T* next to it. If a sentence is false, write *F* next to it. Rewrite each false sentence to make it true.

McGraw-Hill School Division

A Young Nation

A 300-Mile Trip

Suppose you want to plan a family trip from the national capital of the United States to a city that is about 300 miles away. Use the map of the United Sates on page R10 of your social studies textbook to plan the trip.

Find a city about 300 miles from the national capital. Write the name of the city on a sheet of paper. Then list the cities or states you would pass through on your way there.

A Young Nation

Which Map?

Turn to the maps of the Western Hemisphere on pages R20 and R21 of your social studies textbook. On a sheet of paper, write answers to these questions:

- What is the national capital of Costa Rica?
- Which river flows from the Rocky Mountains to the Hudson Bay?
- Which city is farther north—Rio de Janeiro or Brasília?

Tell which map helped you answer each question.

A Young Nation

Following Rivers

Use the map of the United States on page R10 of your social studies textbook to help you follow these directions:

Find a city in Idaho that is not the state capital. Follow the river that is north of the city as it flows toward the Pacific Ocean until you come to the Columbia River. Follow the Columbia River west. What is the first city you reach?

McGraw-Hill School Division

A Young Nation

A State
Fact Sheet

Turn to the map of the United States on page R10 of your social studies textbook. Choose a state. Then write the following information in sentences on a fact sheet about that state:

- **Use latitude and longitude to describe the location of the state.**
- **List the states that border the state.**
- **Name the state capital.**
- **Name other cities in the state.**

Follow the Tropic of Capricorn

Look at the map of the world on page R16 of your social studies textbook. Suppose you know someone who is planning a trip around the world that will begin and end in Australia. Your friend plans to follow the Tropic of Capricorn. Which countries will your friend cross? Write the names of five of the countries on a sheet of paper.

McGraw-Hill School Division

A Young Nation

Latitude, Longitude: True or False?

Turn to the map of Latitude and Longitude on page 41 in your social studies textbook. Then copy these sentences:

- Provo, Utah lies north of 30° N latitude.
- Tennessee's northern border runs along 35° N latitude.
- 80° W longitude runs through Florida.

If a sentence states something true, write *T* next to it. Then rewrite each false sentence to make it true.

McGraw-Hill School Division

A Young Nation

Claimed by the French

Look at the map showing the search for a Northwest Passage on page 176 of your social studies textbook. Suppose you found the journal of a person who lived in an area claimed by the French after 1605. Where might the journal writer have lived? Which explorer might have claimed the area?

Where Are You?

Use the map of the world on page R16 of your social
studies textbook to help you follow this route:
Begin in the country that borders the United
States to the south. Go east in a straight line to a
country in Africa that borders Tunisia and Mali.
Then go northeast to a country that borders
Mongolia and is partly in Europe. Where are you?

McGraw-Hill School Division

Which Hemisphere?

Use the map of the hemispheres on page **G5** of your social studies textbook to find the mystery hemisphere.

This hemisphere includes the continents of North America, South America, and part of Antarctica. It does not include Asia. Which hemisphere is it?

Write the name of the hemisphere on a sheet of paper. Then make up clues for your own mystery hemisphere. Include the names of continents in your clues.

McGraw-Hill School Division

A Captain in the Caribbean

Turn to the map of the world on page R16 of your social studies textbook. Suppose you know the captain of a ship. The captain wants to travel from the tip of Florida to Martinique, and then to Aruba. After visiting Aruba, the captain wants to head back to Florida. What route might the captain take to get from place to place? Write directions so that another captain could follow the same route.

McGraw-Hill School Division

Mystery States

Use the maps of the United States on pages R10 and R12 of your social studies textbook to find two mystery states.

These states are crossed by the Appalachian Mountains on the east. Their western border is formed by the Mississippi River.

Write the names of the mystery states on a sheet of paper. Then make up a clue that would narrow the mystery states from two to one state.

From Portland to Provo

Find Portland, Oregon, on the map of the Western Hemisphere on page R10 of your social studies textbook. Suppose a group of travelers wants to go from Portland, Oregon, to Provo, Utah.

- In what direction should the group travel?
- Which states will the group pass through along the way?
- Will the trip be over or under 600 miles?

McGraw-Hill School Division

A Young Nation

From Maine to Georgia

Use the map of the 13 Colonies on page G11 of your social studies textbook to plan a trip. Suppose a colonial family wants to travel from Maine to Georgia. If they traveled along the western border of the 13 colonies, which colonies would they pass through? Make a list of those colonies.

A Young Nation

Start in Florida

Use the map of the United States on page R10 of your social studies textbook to follow these directions:

Start at the state capital of Florida. Travel northeast for about 300 miles until you come to a capital city. Then travel north about 450 miles to a city in Pennsylvania. Which three cities have you visited?

Now write directions for someone else to follow. Be sure to use direction words and to include the number of miles to travel.

McGraw-Hill School Division

A Young Nation

Different Maps

Use the maps of the Western Hemisphere on pages R20 and R21 of your social studies textbook to complete a chart.

	political	physical
shows the location of cities		
shows land height		
has a map scale		

Copy the chart onto a sheet of paper. Put a check in the box next to each phrase that describes the political map or the physical map.

McGraw-Hill School Division

A Young Nation

Find the Cities

Use the map of the **Western Hemisphere** on page R20 of your social studies textbook to find the following cities:

- **Manaus, Brazil**
- **Rosario, Argentina**
- **Anchorage, Alaska**

List the cities on a sheet of paper. Next to each city, write the lines of latitude and longitude that are closest to that city.

McGraw-Hill School Division

New England Colonies

Use the map of the New England Colonies on page 205 of your social studies textbook to answer the following questions:

- In what year was New Hampshire founded?
- In which colony was Hartford located?
- Which colony was founded first?

Write the answers as sentences in a paragraph about the New England colonies.

A Young Nation

From Georgia

Find **GA (Georgia)** on the map of the 50 United States on page R14 in your social studies textbook. If your friend were traveling from **GA** to other states, in which intermediate direction will your friend travel to each state? Copy and complete each sentence with an intermediate direction word.

From **GA** to **TX**, she travels _____.

From **GA** to **CO**, she travels _____.

From **GA** to **NY**, she travels _____.

From **GA** to **FL**, she travels _____.

McGraw-Hill School Division

A Young Nation

A Pen Pal in South America

Suppose someone received a letter from a pen pal in South America. In the letter the pen pal described his home in a town near the border of Chile.

Use the map of the Western Hemisphere on page R20 of your social studies textbook to find countries where that pen pal might live. Make a list of the countries.

A Young Nation

The Geography of Utah

Find Utah on the map of the United States on page R12 of your social studies textbook. Then copy these sentences:

- The Teton Range crosses Utah from north to south.
- The Great Salt Lake is in southeastern Utah.
- The Great Salt Lake Desert is west of the mountains in Utah.

If a sentence states something true about Utah, write *T* next to it. If a sentence is false, write *F* next to it. Then rewrite each false statement to make it true.

McGraw-Hill School Division

Farther from New York City

Find New York City on the map of the United States on page R10 of your social studies textbook. Then use the map scale to answer this question:

Which city is farther from New York City— Pittsburgh, Pennsylvania, or Providence, Rhode Island?

Write the answer on a sheet of paper. Then write a sentence that gives the distance between New York City and each of the other cities.

McGraw-Hill School Division

The Middle Colonies

Use the map of the Middle Colonies on page 212 of your social studies textbook to answer the following questions:

- In which colony was Trenton located?
- In what year was Delaware founded?
- Which colonies bordered the Atlantic Ocean?

Write the answers as sentences in a paragraph about the Middle colonies.

About California

Find California on the map of the United States on page R12 of your social studies textbook. Then answer these questions:

- What is the name of the mountains found in western California?
- Which deserts are found in southern California?
- Which body of water is on California's western border?

Write the answers to these questions as sentences on a fact sheet about the geography of California. Be sure to write in complete sentences.

McGraw-Hill School Division

A Young Nation

Comparing Continents

Use the physical map of the Western Hemisphere on page R21 of your social studies textbook to complete a chart.

	North America	South America
is completely east of 90°W		
is crossed by the equator		
has mountains in the west		

Copy the chart. Then put a check in the box next to each phrase that describes North America or South America.

McGraw-Hill School Division

A Young Nation

Mystery Country

Use the map of the Western Hemisphere on page R20 of your social studies textbook to find the mystery country.

60°W longitude and 30°S latitude cross in this country.

Write the name of the country on a sheet of paper. Then write a clue for your own mystery country. Be sure to use latitude and longitude in the clue.

A Young Nation

120°E
Longitude

Look at the map of the world on page R16 of your social studies textbook. Find 120°E longitude. Where does this line of longitude meet the equator? Where does 120°E longitude meet the Arctic Circle?

McGraw-Hill School Division

From Santa Fe to Los Angeles

Use the maps of the United States on pages R10 and R12 of your social studies textbook to finish this story:

Jan and her family left Santa Fe, New Mexico, and drove west toward Arizona, crossing the _____ River. At the border of Arizona and California, they crossed the _____ River. Then they drove across the _____ Desert before reaching Los Angeles.

Copy the story onto a sheet of paper. Write the name of a physical feature to complete each sentence.

McGraw-Hill School Division

A Young Nation

Europe: True or False?

Turn to the map of the world on page R16 of your social studies textbook. Then copy these sentences:
- Sweden is northwest of Poland.
- The United Kingdom is south of France.
- Spain, France, Italy, and Greece border the Mediterranean Sea.

If a sentence states something true about Europe, write *T* next to it. If a sentence is false, write *F* next to it. Rewrite each false sentence so it says something true about Europe.

Where Is Poland?

Look at the map of the world on page R16 of your social studies textbook. Find Poland. Write three sentences describing the country's location. In one of the sentences, tell which countries border Poland.

From Atlanta

Find Atlanta, Georgia, on the map of the Western Hemisphere on page R20 of your social studies textbook. If you wanted to get to each of the cities named, in which intermediate direction would you travel? Copy and complete each sentence with an intermediate direction word.

From Atlanta to Houston, travel _____.

From Atlanta to Miami, travel _____.

From Atlanta to Boston, travel _____.

From Atlanta to Portland, travel _____.

A Young Nation

The Southeast Region

Use the map of the Regions of the United States on page 29 in your social studies textbook to answer these questions:

- Which states make up the Southwest region?
- How many states are part of the Southeast region?
- Which regions border on the Atlantic Ocean?

A Young Nation

Mystery Traveler

Use the map of the United States on page R10 of your social studies textbook to find the mystery traveler.

The mystery traveler is in a city very near 80°W longitude. In which three cities could she be?

Write the names of the cities on a sheet of paper.

Then write one more clue that would narrow the cities from two to one city.

A Young Nation

The Southern Colonies

Use the map of the Southern Colonies on page 218 in your social studies textbook to answer the following questions:

- In what year was Maryland founded?
- In which colony was Savannah?
- In which colony was the James River?

Write the answers as sentences.

A Young Nation

A Trip Along Lake Erie

Suppose your family took a trip along Lake Erie. Use the map of the United States on page R10 of your social studies textbook to describe the trip.

Which four states might you visit? About how many miles long is Lake Erie from west to northeast? Which lake is northeast of Lake Erie? Write the answers as sentences in a paragraph about your family trip.

Mystery State

Turn to the map of the United States on page R10 of your social studies textbook. Use these clues to find the mystery state:

This state is bordered on the southwest by Georgia.

One of its cities is located near 80°W longitude. Write the name of the mystery state on a sheet of paper. Then make up clues for your own mystery state. Include directions and latitude or longitude in your clues.

A Young Nation

Elevation in New York

Turn to the elevation map of New York on page 214 of your social studies textbook. Which color shows areas that are between 0 and 500 feet above sea level? Which cities are located in areas that have such an elevation?

McGraw-Hill School Division

A Young Nation

Which Country?

Use the map of the **Western Hemisphere** on page R20 of your social studies textbook to find the mystery country.

This country is crossed by 120°W longitude and 60°N latitude. Which country is it?

Write clues for your own mystery country. Be sure to use latitude and longitude in one of your clues.

A Young Nation

90°W
Longitude

Turn to the map of the United States on page R10 of your social studies textbook. Find 90°W longitude.

Which states are crossed by 90°W longitude? List them on a sheet of paper in order from north to south.

Finding Elevation and Relief

Turn to the elevation and relief maps of Washington on page G10 of your social studies textbook. Find the following cities:

- Spokane
- Seattle
- Olympia
- Yakima

List the cities on a sheet of paper. Next to each city, write whether it is located in an area of high, moderate, or low relief.

McGraw-Hill School Division

A Young Nation

A Pen Pal in Africa

Suppose you received a letter from a pen pal in Africa. In the letter your pen pal described her home in a town on the southeast coast of Africa on the Indian Ocean.

Use the map of the world on page R16 of your social studies textbook to find three countries where your pen pal might live. Make a list of the countries.

Mystery Hemisphere

Use the map of the hemispheres on page G5 of your social studies textbook to find the mystery hemisphere.

> This hemisphere includes the continents of North America and Europe. It does not include Antarctica. Which hemisphere is it?

Write the name of the hemisphere on a sheet of paper. Then make up clues for your own mystery hemisphere. Include the names of continents in your clues.

McGraw-Hill School Division

A Young Nation

Find the Country

Turn to the world map on page R16 of your social studies textbook. Use the lines of latitude and longitude to find the locations listed below:

- 20°S latitude, 140°E longitude
- 60°N latitude, 140°E longitude
- 60°N latitude, 40°E longitude
- 0° latitude, 40°E longitude

On a sheet of paper, write the name of the country at each location.

McGraw-Hill School Division

A Young Nation

Mystery Country

Use the map of the world on page R16 of your social studies textbook to find the mystery country.

This country is a part of a peninsula. It is bordered by Portugal on the west and France on the northeast. Which country is it?

Write the name of the country on a sheet of paper. Then write clues for your own mystery country. Be sure to use geographic terms in your clues.

A Great Lakes Vacation

Suppose you know a group of people who are planning a vacation. The people want to visit a state where they will be able to spend time at the shore of one of the Great Lakes. Use the map of the United States on page R10 of your social studies textbook to help you figure out which states the people might visit. Make a list of the states.

McGraw-Hill School Division

Mystery States and a Desert

Turn to the map of the United States on page R12 of your social studies textbook. Use this clue to find the mystery states:

The Sonora Desert is in the southern part of these states.

Which two states could the mystery states be? Write both names on a sheet of paper. Then write a clue that narrows the mystery states down to one state.

McGraw-Hill School Division

State Abbreviations

Use the map of the 50 United States on page R14 of your social studies textbook to find abbreviations for each state. Suppose Mrs. Harmon wrote eight letters to friends in different states. Copy each state name and write the abbreviation she used.

Montana _____   Mississippi _____

Washington _____   Maine _____

Georgia _____   Massachusetts _____

Alaska ____   Iowa _____

Hawaii _____

A Young Nation

Mystery Countries

Use the map of the **Western Hemisphere** on page R20 of your social studies textbook to find the mystery countries.

These countries are crossed by the equator. Which three countries could they be?

Write the names of the countries on a sheet of paper. Then write another clue to narrow the mystery countries from three to one country.

A look at
Some States

Turn to the maps of the United States on pages R10 and R12 of your social studies textbook. Find North Dakota, Maine, and New Mexico.

- Which river runs through North Dakota?
- What is the name of the mountain range in Maine?
- What is the name of the river in central New Mexico?

Write the answers to these questions as sentences.

McGraw-Hill School Division

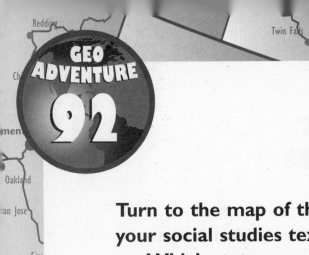

30°N
Latitude

Turn to the map of the United States on page R10 of your social studies textbook. Find 30°N latitude.

Which states are crossed by 30°N latitude? List them on a sheet of paper in order from west to east.

A Young Nation

The Battle of Yorktown

Look at the map showing the Battle of Yorktown on page 337 of your social studies textbook. Which of the following questions can you answer using the map key?

- Which cities are south of the James River?
- Which fleet was located near Cape Charles?
- About how far from Yorktown is Jamestown?
- Which forces surrounded Yorktown?
- Which rivers flow into Chesapeake Bay?

A Young Nation

Indiana's Corn and Dairy Farms

Look at the map of Indiana's Corn and Dairy Farms on page G8 of your social studies textbook. Then answer these questions:

- Where in Indiana is the Dairy-farming area?
- If you lived near Monticello, which type of farms would you see?
- If you lived near Ft. Wayne, which type of farms would you see?

Use the answers to these questions to write a fact sheet about corn and dairy farms in Indiana.

McGraw-Hill School Division

A Young Nation

Land Near
the Lakes

Turn to the elevation map of New York on page 214 of your social studies textbook. What is the elevation of land bordering Lake Ontario to the south? Is the land bordering Lake Erie higher or lower than the land near Lake Ontario? Explain how you figured out the answer.

Mystery Traveler on Vacation

Use the inset map of Central America and the West Indies on page R16 of your social studies textbook to find the mystery traveler.

The mystery traveler is taking a vacation on an island in the Caribbean Sea. This island is east of 60°W longitude. On which island is he?

A Young Nation

The American Revolution

Turn to the historical map showing **Battles of the American Revolution** on page 332 of your social studies textbook. Then answer the following questions:

- In which state did the battle at Camden take place?
- In what year was the battle at Saratoga fought?
- In which states did battles take place in 1775?

Write the answers as sentences in a paragraph about the battles of the American Revolution.

McGraw-Hill School Division

A Young Nation

Closer to Knoxville, Tennessee

Find Knoxville, Tennessee, on the map of the United States on page R10 of your social studies textbook. Then use the map scale to answer this question:

Which city is closer to Knoxville, Tennessee— Raleigh, North Carolina, or Atlanta, Georgia?

Write the answer on a sheet of paper. Then write sentences that tell about how many miles it is between Knoxville, Tennessee, and the other cities.

McGraw-Hill School Division

A Young Nation

The Southeast

Look at the physical map of the United States on page R12 in your social studies textbook. Find the Atlantic Coastal Plain. Then answer the following questions:

- Which mountain range runs from north to south in the eastern United States?
- What region is east of the Appalachian Mountains?
- Which mountains are to the west of the Appalachian Mountains?
- How high is Mt. Mitchell?

McGraw-Hill School Division

100°W Longitude

Turn to the map of the world on page R16 of your social studies textbook. Find 100°W longitude.

Which countries above the equator are crossed by 100°W longitude? List them on a sheet of paper in order from north to south.

McGraw-Hill School Division

A Young Nation

The Northwest Territory

Look at the map of the Northwest Territory on page 344 of your social studies textbook. Which states were formed from the Northwest Territory? Which country had claimed land west of the Mississippi River? Which country had claimed land north of the river?

McGraw-Hill School Division

A Drive from Buffalo, New York

Use the map of the United States on page R10 of your social studies textbook to finish this story:

Tim and his family left their home in Buffalo, New York, and drove _____ to Norfolk, Virginia. From there they drove _____ to Charlotte, North Carolina. Then they drove _____ to Frankfort, Kentucky.

Copy the story onto a sheet of paper. Use a direction word to complete each sentence.

A Young Nation

Regions:
True or False?

Turn to the Regions of the United States map on page 29 of your social studies textbook. Then copy these sentences:

- Texas is in the Southwest.
- Tennessee is in the Middle West.
- Oregon is in the Northeast.
- Kansas is in the Middle West.

If a statement is true, write *T* next to it. Then rewrite each false statement to make it true.

Mystery Hemisphere

Use the map of the hemispheres on page **G5** of your social studies textbook to find the mystery hemisphere.

This hemisphere includes the continents of Australia, Antarctica, and parts of Africa, Asia, and South America. It does not include Europe or North America. Which hemisphere is it?

Make up clues for your own mystery hemisphere. Include the names of continents in your clues.

A Young Nation

Farther from Philadelphia

Find Philadelphia on the road map of Pennsylvania on page G11 of your social studies textbook. Then use the map scale to answer this question:

> Which city is farther from Philadelphia—Pottstown or Lancaster?

Write the answer on a sheet of paper. Then write a sentence that tells the distance between Philadelphia and each of the cities.

McGraw-Hill School Division

A Young Nation

The Lewis and Clark Expedition

Turn to the map of the Louisiana Purchase on page 381 of your social studies textbook. Find the route of the Lewis and Clark Expedition. Then answer these questions:

- Where did the expedition begin and end?
- Which mountains did it cross?
- Through which land areas did the expedition travel?

Write the answers as sentences in a paragraph about the Lewis and Clark Expedition.

McGraw-Hill School Division

A Young Nation

From Gary, Indiana

Turn to the map of the United States on page R10 of your social studies textbook. Suppose you have a friend who wants to travel from Gary, Indiana, to Wichita, Kansas. In which direction should your friend travel? About how many miles will she have to go?

About how many miles will she have to go?

After visiting Wichita, your friend wants to travel to Tulsa, Oklahoma. About how many miles will she have to go?

McGraw-Hill School Division

GEO ADVENTURE 107

A Young Nation

Sail from Puerto Rico

Look at the inset map of Central America and the West Indies on page R16 of your social studies textbook. Find Puerto Rico. Then answer these questions:

- In which direction would you sail to get from Puerto Rico to St. Lucia?
- In which direction would you sail to get from St. Lucia to Trinidad?

A Capital Adventure

Look at the map of the United States on page R10 in your social studies textbook. Suppose your friend will visit four state capitals—Tallahassee, Raleigh, Montgomery, and Richmond. Which states will your friend visit? List each state capital and the state name.

McGraw-Hill School Division

A Young Nation

Where's the Mystery Traveler?

Use the map of the United States on page R10 of your social studies textbook to find the mystery traveler.

The mystery traveler is in a city just west of 110°W longitude and just north of 40°N latitude. The city is not the state capital. Where is she?

A Young Nation

What Region Is It?

Turn to the Regions of the United States map on page 29 of your social studies textbook.

- **In which region do you live if you live in Idaho?**
- **In which region do you live if you live in Connecticut?**
- **If you traveled from Idaho to Connecticut, through all of which region would you cross?**

A Young Nation

Cities in North America

Turn to the map of the **Western Hemisphere** on page R20 of your social studies textbook. Find the national capitals of Canada, the United States, and Mexico.

Write the name of each country and its national capital on a sheet of paper.

A Trail to the West

Turn to the map of Trails to the West on page 431 of your social studies textbook. Suppose you found the journal of someone who traveled with a group of people from Independence to Salt Lake City. Which trail might the people have followed? Which fort might they have passed along the way? What other things might the people have seen?

A Young Nation

States That Left the Union

Look at the map of the Union and the Confederacy on page 474 of your social studies textbook. Which slave states that left the Union bordered states that stayed in the Union? Which slave state that left the Union bordered territories?

Elevation and Relief

Turn to the elevation and relief maps on page G10 of your social studies textbook. Then copy these sentences:

- **Both maps show the location of mountain ranges.**
- **The relief map shows the height above sea level of the Columbia Plateau.**
- **The relief map shows that Olympia has low relief.**

If a sentence states something true, write *T* next to it. If a sentence is false, write *F* next to it. Rewrite each false statement to make it true.

McGraw-Hill School Division

Using Intermediate Directions

Look at the map of Louisiana on page G6 of your social studies textbook. Suppose a family in Shreveport took a trip to Baton Rouge. In which direction would they have traveled?

Suppose another family traveled from Lafayette to New Orleans. In which direction would they have traveled?

A Young Nation

Wisconsin and Louisiana

Use the map of the United States on page R10 of your social studies textbook to complete the chart.

	Wisconsin	Louisiana
is south of Illinois		
is crossed by 90°W longitude		
is north of 40°N latitude		

Copy the chart onto a sheet of paper. Put a check in the box next to each phrase that describes Wisconsin or Louisiana.

McGraw-Hill School Division

A Young Nation

Latitude and Longitude

Turn to the world map on page R16 of your social studies textbook. Use the lines of latitude and longitude to find the following locations:
- 40°N latitude, 100°W longitude
- 40°N latitude, 140°E longitude
- 20°S latitude, 20°E longitude
- 0° latitude, 20°E longitude

On a sheet of paper, write the name of the country at each location.

A Young Nation

A Trip
from Peoria

Look at the map of the United States on pages R10
and R11 of your social studies textbook. Suppose you
have a friend who wants to travel from Peoria, Illinois,
to Frankfort, Kentucky. From Frankfort, she wants to
go to Newark, New Jersey.

   Which states will your friend pass through along
the way? How many miles will she travel between
each city?

McGraw-Hill School Division

Traveling in Pennsylvania

Use the road map of Pennsylvania on page G11 of your social studies textbook to find out which cities the mystery traveler visited.

The mystery traveler started at Allentown. She drove north on Interstate 476 until it crossed Interstate 80. Then she drove west on Interstate 80 until she reached state highway 219. She traveled south on that highway about 60 miles.

On a sheet of paper, write the name of the city where the mystery traveler ended her trip.

A Young Nation

Which Distance Is Shorter?

Use the map of the Southwest on page 31 of your social studies textbook to answer this question:

Which distance is shorter?

From Santa Fe, New Mexico, to Phoenix, Arizona?

From Santa Fe, New Mexico, to Austin, Texas?

Write the answer on a sheet of paper. Then write a sentence that tells the number of miles between the two cities in each pair.

McGraw-Hill School Division

A Young Nation

Mystery State Code

Turn to the map of the United States on page R10 of your social studies textbook. Suppose the mystery traveler gave you this coded message about a trip he was planning:

- I'm going to 40°N latitude and 110°W.
- Which state will I be in?
- I'm going to 40°N latitude and 90°W longitude.
- Which state will I be in?

A Young Nation

Using a Map Key

Turn to the map of Indiana's Corn and Dairy Farms on page G8 of your social studies textbook. Which of the following questions can you answer using the map key?

- Which products are produced in Monticello?
- What is the capital of Indiana?
- About how far from the state capital is Bedford?
- Is corn grown east of Muncie?
- Which river forms the southern border of Indiana?

McGraw-Hill School Division

A National Forest

Look at the map of Francis Marion National Forest on page G8 of your social studies textbook. Answer these questions:

- **Where is the forest located?**
- **In which direction is Jamestown?**
- **How many ranger stations does the forest have?**

Write the answers as sentences on a fact sheet about Francis Marion National Forest. Then add one more fact that you can learn from the map.

State Capitals Chart

Use the map of the United States on page R10 of your social studies textbook to complete this chart.

City	State Capital
Reno, Nevada	
Madison, Wisconsin	
Memphis, Tennessee	
Des Moines, Iowa	

Copy the chart onto a sheet of paper. Put a check next to each city if it is a state capital.

McGraw-Hill School Division

A Young Nation

Major
Roads, 1860

Turn to the maps of Transportation in the Eastern
United States in 1860 on page 413 of your social
studies textbook. Suppose you needed to send goods
from Richmond to New Orleans. On which major road
could you travel? From Cincinnati could you travel by
river to Memphis or Nashville?

McGraw-Hill School Division

A Young Nation

From Concord, New Hampshire

Suppose you have a friend who is traveling on a bus from Concord, New Hampshire, to New Haven, Connecticut. Use the map of the Northeast on page 34 of your social studies textbook to describe your friend's trip.

- In which direction will your friend travel?
- About how many miles will your friend travel?
- If your friend goes on to Philadephia, Pennsylvania, in which direction will he go?

A Young Nation

Trails:
True or False?

Turn to the map of Trails to the West on page 431 of
your social studies textbook. Then copy these
sentences:

- Donner Pass was located along the Oregon Trail.
- Whitman's Mission was located near Split Rock.
- The Old Spanish Trail led to San Francisco.
- Ft. Laramie was located near Soda Springs.

If a sentence states something true, write *T* next to it.
If a sentence is false, write *F* next to it. Rewrite each
false sentence to make it true.

Facts from Different Maps

Turn to the political map of the United States on page R10 of your social studies textbook. Find New Mexico. What can you learn about New Mexico by studying the map? On a sheet of paper, write as many facts as you can.

Then turn to the physical map of the United States on page R12. What more can you learn about New Mexico from this map? Add more facts to your list.

McGraw-Hill School Division

A Young Nation

Find the Cities

Use the map of the **Western Hemisphere** on page **R20** of your social studies textbook to find the following cities:

- **Rosario, Argentina**
- **Houston, United States**
- **Nuuk, Greenland**

List the cities on a sheet of paper. Next to each city, write the lines of latitude and longitude that are closest to that city.

McGraw-Hill School Division

A Young Nation

Where Are These Cities?

Use the map of the United States on page R10 of your social studies textbook to find these cities:
- **Reno, Nevada**
- **Jacksonville, Florida**
- **Honolulu, Hawaii**

List the cities on a sheet of paper. Next to each city, write the numbers of the lines of latitude and longitude that are closest to that city.

McGraw-Hill School Division

Memphis, Tennessee

Find Memphis, Tennessee, on the map of the United States on page R10 of your social studies textbook. Then answer these questions:

- Which city is closest to Memphis?
- Which city is directly south of Memphis?
- Which city is directly east of Memphis?

Choose from the following cities for the answers:

Charlotte, North Carolina

New Orleans, Louisiana

St. Louis, Missouri

A Young Nation

Follow the Directions

Use the map of the United States on page R10 of your social studies textbook to follow these directions:

Start at 40°N latitude, 110°W longitude. Go 30 degrees east. Then go 10 degrees south. Now go 10 degrees west.

In which city are you? What is the latitude and longitude of the city?

McGraw-Hill School Division

A Young Nation

Mystery Traveler

Use the map of the 50 United States on page R14 of your social studies textbook to find out where the mystery traveler went.

The mystery traveler started his trip in **KS**. He flew northeast to **PA**. Then he flew south to **NC**. Then he flew west to **NM**.

On a sheet of paper, write the names of the states the mystery traveler visited.

A Young Nation

Mystery
Hemisphere

Use the map of the hemispheres on page G5 of your
social studies textbook to find the mystery hemisphere.
This hemisphere includes all of Africa and Australia.
It does not include North America. Which
hemisphere is it?
Write the name of the hemisphere on a sheet of paper.
Then make up clues for your own mystery hemisphere.
Include the names of continents in your clues.

Farthest Apart

Use the map of the Western Hemisphere on page R20 of your social studies textbook to answer this question:

Which pair of cities are farthest apart?

Mexico City, Mexico, and Denver, Colorado?

Lima, Peru, and Phoenix, Arizona?

Manaus, Brazil, and Portland, Oregon?

Write the answer on a sheet of paper.

A Young Nation

A Northern Border

Turn to the map of the United States on page R10 of your social studies textbook. Use the map scale to answer these questions:

- **How long is the northern border of Arizona?**
- **Is it longer or shorter than the eastern border of Nevada?**
- **Is it longer or shorter than the northern border of Utah?**

McGraw-Hill School Division

Start in Washington

Use the map of the United States on page R10 of your social studies textbook to follow these directions: Start at Seattle, Washington. Travel southeast for about 600 miles to a city in Idaho. Then travel about 300 miles east to a city in Wyoming. Which three cities have you visited?

McGraw-Hill School Division

A Young Nation

Mystery Country

Use the world map on page R16 of your social studies textbook to find the mystery country.

This country is made up of islands in the Pacific Ocean. It is crossed by 40°N latitude.

Write the name of the mystery country on a sheet of paper. Then make up clues for your own mystery country. Include geographic terms and latitude or longitude in your clues.

McGraw-Hill School Division

A Young Nation

Plan a River Trip

Suppose a group of people were planning to take a river trip from Casper, Wyoming, to Knoxville, Tennessee. Use the maps of the United States on pages R10 and R12 of your social studies textbook to help plan the trip.

- Which cities might the group pass along the way?
- What kinds of landforms might the group see?

A Young Nation

What Am I?

Use the physical map of the United States on page R12 of your social studies textbook to solve this riddle:

I am a mountain range directly north of the Central Plains. I am directly west of Lake Superior. I am located to the south of Canada. What am I?

Write the answer on a sheet of paper. Then use the map to make up a riddle of your own.

McGraw-Hill School Division

A Young Nation

Mystery Travel in Europe

Turn to the inset map of Europe on page R16 of your social studies textbook. Suppose the mystery traveler gave you this message about a trip to Europe:

What four countries in Europe will the mystery traveler visit when traveling northeast from Spain to Belarus.

The Great Basin

Turn to the physical map of the United States on page R12 of your social studies textbook. Then answer these questions about the Great Basin:

- Which mountains are east of the Great Basin?
- Which plateau is north of the Great Basin?
- Which deserts are south of the Great Basin?

Write the answers as sentences in a paragraph about the Great Basin.

A Young Nation

Which Is Nearer to Burlington?

Look at the map of the United States on page R10 of your social studies textbook. Find Burlington, Vermont. Then use the map scale to answer this question:

> **Which is nearer to Burlington—Albany, New York, or Buffalo, New York?**

Write the answer on a sheet of paper. Then write a sentence that tells the distance between Burlington and each of the other places.

The Tropic of Cancer

Turn to the map of the world on page R16 of your social studies textbook. Suppose you know someone who plans to follow the Tropic of Cancer around the world. Your friend plans to begin and end his trip in China. He will travel west. Which countries and bodies of water will your friend cross?

A Young Nation

A Pen Pal

Suppose you received a letter from a pen pal in Europe. In the letter your pen pal described her life in a town near the coast of the Baltic Sea.

Use the inset map of Europe on page R17 of your social studies textbook to find countries where your pen pal might live. Make a list of the countries.

Mystery City

Use the map of the United States on page R10 of your social studies textbook to find the mystery city. Here are the clues:

> **This state capital is located on the Arkansas River. It is southeast of Fort Smith. What is the mystery city?**

Write the name of the mystery city. Then write clues for your own mystery city. Use the map to help you write one of your clues.

Facts About Mexico

Turn to the political map of the Western Hemisphere on page R20 of your social studies textbook. Find Mexico. What can you learn about Mexico by studying the map? Write as many facts as you can.

Then look at the physical map of the Western Hemisphere on page R21. What more can you learn about Mexico from this map? Add two more facts to your list.

A Young Nation

Egypt Fact Sheet

Turn to the world map on page R16 of your social studies textbook. Suppose you are making a fact sheet for a group of travelers on their way to Egypt. Write the following information on the fact sheet:

- **Use latitude and longitude to describe the location of Egypt.**
- **Name some of the countries that border Egypt.**

A Young Nation

The World Traveler

Use the map of the world on page R16 of your social studies textbook to follow the path of the world traveler.

The world traveler started his trip in a country that borders Pakistan, China, and Nepal. Then he traveled north in a straight line until he reached the Arctic Circle.

In which country did the world traveler start?

McGraw-Hill School Division

A Young Nation

Answer Key

1. The maps should accurately reflect the shape of the state in which students live, include a compass rose, and include a label that shows the correct location of the state capital. The maps should be colored and have an appropriate title.

2. Idaho; to check the accuracy of their clues, you may want to have students read their clues aloud and solve one another's mystery states. At least one clue should contain a direction word and distances in miles.

3. Students should accurately list the states they would cross in order if they were traveling from their state capital to Nashville, Tennessee. Students should also provide the capital of each state on the list.

4. Reno, Nevada: 40°N latitude, 120°W longitude; Springfield, Illinois: 40°N latitude, 90°W longitude; New Orleans, Louisiana: 30°N latitude, 90°W longitude

5. Russia

6. Annapolis, Maryland; Chesapeake Bay

7. Students' answers should include the following information: Alaska is bordered by the Arctic Ocean, the Bering Sea, the Gulf of Alaska, and the Pacific Ocean; Juneau is the capital of Alaska; Mt. McKinley is about 500 miles from the west coast of Alaska.

8. Texas, Louisiana, Mississippi, Alabama, Florida

9. Maine; to check the accuracy of their clues, you may want to have students read their clues aloud and solve one another's mystery state. At least one clue should contain information about landforms.

10. The first and third sentences are false and can be rewritten as follows: lines of latitude measure the distance from the equator; latitude lines extend east and west.

11. Students' charts should include the following information: North America—Northern and Western hemispheres; South America—Southern and Western hemispheres; Europe—Northern and Eastern hemispheres; Africa—Southern, Northern, and Eastern hemispheres; Asia—Southern, Eastern, and Northern hemispheres; Australia—Southern and Eastern hemispheres; Antarctica—Southern, Western, and Eastern hemispheres.

12. Peru; to check the accuracy of their clues, you may want to have students read their clues aloud and solve one another's mystery countries. At least one clue should contain information about latitude and longitude.

13. Students' paragraphs should include the following information: lines of latitude extend

from east to west; lines of latitude measure the distance from the equator; lines of longitude extend from north to south; lines of longitude begin and end at the Prime Meridian.

14. Porto Alegre, Brazil; Brazil, Bolivia, Argentina, and Brazil are passed through along the way.

15. Students' answers should accurately reflect the location of their state.

16. North American countries that border the Pacific Ocean and are almost completely west of 90°W longitude include Canada, the United States, Mexico, and Guatamala.

17. 60°N latitude, 150° W longitude—Anchorage, Alaska; 30°N latitude, 120°W longitude—Los Angeles, California; 0° latitude, 60°W longitude—Manaus, Brazil

18. Southeast; California, Nevada, Utah, Colorado; Northeast

19. Students' route descriptions may include the following bodies of water: Pacific Ocean,

Atlantic Ocean, Indian Ocean, Arctic Ocean.

20. The third sentence is true. The other sentences can be rewritten as follows: the scale on both maps shows miles and kilometers; the scale on map A shows that one inch equals 260 miles, and the scale on map B shows that one inch equals 130 miles.

21. New Jersey, Pennsylvania, Ohio, Indiana, Illinois, Missouri, Kansas/Nebraska (border), Colorado, Utah, Nevada, California

22. Borders an ocean—Georgia; is north of 40°N latitude—North Dakota; is east of 90°W longitude—Georgia

23. Arctic; Aleut; Plains; Basin and Plateau, Southwest, Eastern Woodlands

24. Answers may include: Reno and Carson City, Nevada; Provo, Utah; Denver, Colorado; Springfield, Illinois; Indianapolis, Indiana; Columbus, Ohio; Wheeling, West Virginia; Harrisburg, Pennsylvania;

Philadelphia, Pennsylvania; Trenton, New Jersey.

25. Route 322. Directions to Williamsport should include: travel northeast from State College on Route 220.

26. Colorado River

27. Students should include four of the following mountain ranges. Mountain ranges west of 90°W longitude include: Brooks Range, Alaska Range, Cascade Range, Coast Ranges, Sierra Nevada, Rocky Mountains, Teton Range, and the Wasatch Range. Mountain ranges east of 90°W longitude include: Appalachian Mountains, Allegheny Mountains, Adirondack Mountains, Green Mountains, and White Mountains.

28. Students might write the following: White Mountains, Mt. Washington, Green Mountains, Cape Cod, Hudson River, Long Island, Lake Ontario, Lake Erie, Lake Huron, Lake Michigan, Lake Superior.

29. Montana, Wyoming, Utah, Arizona; to check the accuracy of their clues, you may want to

have students read their clues aloud and find one another's mystery states.

30. South Dakota; North Carolina; Florida.

31. The clues should include the following information: the location of the state, the names of nearby states, and the state capital. To check the accuracy of their clues, you may want to have students read their clues aloud and find one another's mystery states.

32. The first and third sentences can be answered using the map key.

33. shows changes in Earth's surface—elevation, relief; uses shading to show differences in land height—relief; shows land height above sea level—elevation

34. first voyage; San Salvador; 1493; fourth; south; Jamaica; Central America

35. Tallahasee is about 450 miles southeast of Nashville; Atlanta is less than 300 miles southeast of Nashville; Baton Rouge is about

450 miles southwest of Atlanta.

36. Egypt; Africa

37. Canada, United States, Mexico, Guatamala, El Salvador, Nicaragua, Costa Rica, Panama

38. The equator crosses Ecuador, Colombia, and Brazil; Venezuela is north of the equator and west of Guyana. Peru and Bolivia are entirely between the equator and the Tropic of Capricorn.

39. The Gulf of Mexico; the Atlantic Ocean; the Coastal Plains

40. Students' paragraphs should include the following information: the Rocky Mountains are found in North America; the Rocky Mountains extend from north to south; Canada and the United States.

41. Richmond; Alabama; 300; north

42. The second sentence is true. The other sentences can be rewritten as follows: Mt. Rainier is the fourth tallest mountain in the United States; Mt. Rainier is about 150 miles from Canada.

43. All three sentences are false and can be rewritten as follows: the map shows the 13 colonies in the 1700s; Maine was part of the Massachusetts colony; there were three different groups of colonies in the 1700s.

44. Students' directions should accurately describe how to get from Washington, D.C., to a city that is about 300 miles away. Students should list the cities and/or states they would pass through along the way. You might suggest students use a ruler or map scale strip when determining distances.

45. Students' sentences should include the following information: the national capital of Costa Rica is San José (political map); the Saskatchewan River flows from the Rocky Mountains to the Hudson Bay (physical map); Brasília is farther north than Rio de Janeiro (political map).

46. Portland, Oregon

47. On their fact sheets, students should include the following

154

information: the state's latitude and longitude, the other states that border the chosen state, the state's capital, and other cities in the state.

48. Students' answers should include five of the following: Australia, Chile, Argentina, Paraguay, Brazil, Namibia, Botswana, South Africa, Mozambique, Madagascar.

49. The first sentence is true. The next two are false and can be written as follows: Tennessee's southern border runs along 35° N latitude. 80°W longitude does not run through Florida.

50. Quebec, Montreal, Port Royal, or Fort Caroline; Carter or Cabot

51. Begin in Mexico; go east to Algeria; go northeast to Russia.

52. Western Hemisphere; to check the accuracy of their clues, you may want to have students read their clues aloud and find one another's mystery hemispheres.

53. Students should accurately describe the following route:

travel southeast from the tip of Florida to Martinique; from Martinique, southwest to Aruba; from Aruba, northwest to Florida.

54. Kentucky or Tennessee; to check the accuracy of their clues, you may want to have students read their clues aloud and find one another's mystery states.

55. Southeast; the group will pass through Oregon, Idaho, Nevada, and Utah; over 600 miles

56. They would pass through Maine, New Hampshire, New York, Pennsylvania, Maryland, Virginia, North Carolina, South Carolina, and Georgia.

57. Tallahassee, Florida; Columbia, South Carolina; Pittsburgh, Pennsylvania. To check the accuracy of their directions, you may want to have students listen to and follow one another's directions.

58. shows the location of cities—political map; shows the differences in land height—physical map; has a map scale—political map, physical map

59. Manaus, Brazil: 0° latitude, 60°W longitude; Rosario, Argentina: 30°S latitude, 60°W longitude; Anchorage, Alaska: 60°N latitude, 150°W longitude

60. Students' paragraphs should include the following information: New Hampshire was founded in 1680; Hartford was located in the Connecticut colony; the Massachusetts colony was founded first.

61. From GA to TX, she travels southwest. From GA to CO, she travels northwest. From GA to NY, she travels northwest. From GA to FL, she travels southwest.

62. Peru, Bolivia, Argentina

63. The third sentence is true. The other sentences can be rewritten as follows: the Wasatch Range crosses Utah from north to south; the Great Salt Lake is in northwestern Utah.

64. Pittsburgh, Pennsylvania. Pittsburgh is about 300 miles from New York City, New York. Providence, Rhode Island, is about 150 miles from New York City.

McGraw-Hill School Division

65. Students' paragraphs should include the following information: Trenton was located in the New Jersey colony; Delaware was founded in 1704; New York, New Jersey, and Delaware bordered the Atlantic Ocean.

66. Students' fact sheets should include the following information: the Coast Ranges are found in western California; the Mojave Desert and the Sonora Desert are found in northern California; the Pacific Ocean borders California to the west.

67. is completely east of 90°W longitude—South America; is crossed by the equator—South America; has mountains in the west—North America, South America

68. Argentina; to check the accuracy of their clues, you may want to have students read their clues aloud and find one another's mystery countries.

69. Indonesia; Russia

70. Rio Grande River; Colorado River; Mojave Desert

71. The third sentence is true. The other sentences can be rewritten as follows: Sweden is north of Poland; the United Kingdom is north of France.

72. Students' sentences might include some of the following: Poland is south of the Baltic Sea; Poland is east of 10°E longitude; Poland is bordered by Germany, Czech Republic, Slovakia, Ukraine, Belarus, Lithuania, and Russia.

73. From Atlanta to Houston, travel southwest. From Atlanta to Miami, travel southeast. From Atlanta to Boston, travel northeast. From Atlanta to Portland, travel northwest.

74. Arizona, New Mexico, Oklahoma, and Texas; 12 states are part of the Southeast region; the Northeast and Southeast border on the Atlantic Ocean.

75. Pittsburgh, Pennsylvania; Charleston, South Carolina; Miami, Florida. To check the accuracy of their clues, you may want to have students read their clues aloud and find the

location of one another's mystery travelers.

76. Maryland was founded in 1634; Savannah was in Georgia; James River was in Virginia.

77. Michigan, Ohio, Pennsylvania, New York; about 300 miles; Lake Ontario.

78. South Carolina; Columbia; to check the accuracy of their clues, you may want to have students read their clues aloud and find one another's mystery states.

79. dark green; Rochester, Syracuse, Albany, and New York City

80. Canada; to check the accuracy of their clues, you may want to have students read their clues aloud and find one another's mystery countries.

81. Michigan, Wisconsin, Illinois, Missouri, Arkansas, Tennessee, Mississippi, Louisiana

82. Spokane—moderate relief; Seattle—low relief; Olympia—low relief; Yakima—moderate relief

156

83. Tanzania, Mozambique, South Africa.

84. Northern Hemisphere; to check the accuracy of their clues, you may want to have students read their clues aloud and find one another's mystery hemispheres.

85. 20°S latitude, 140°E longitude: Australia; 60°N latitude, 140°E longitude: Russia; 60°N latitude, 40°E longitude: Russia; 0° latitude, 40°E longitude: Kenya

86. Spain; to check the accuracy of their clues, you may want to have students read their clues aloud and find one another's mystery countries.

87. Minnesota, Michigan, Wisconsin, Illinois, Indiana, Ohio, Pennsylvania, New York

88. California, Arizona; to check the accuracy of their clues, you may want to have students read their clues aloud and find one another's mystery states.

89. MT, WA, GA, AK, HI, MS, ME, MA, IA

90. Ecuador, Colombia, Brazil; to check the accuracy of their clues, you may want to have students read their clues aloud and find one another's mystery countries.

91. Students' sentences should include the following information: the Missouri River runs through North Dakota; the White Mountains are in Maine; the Rio Grande runs through New Mexico.

92. Texas, Louisiana, Florida

93. The first, second, and fourth questions can be answered using the map key.

94. Students' fact sheets should include the following information: dairy farms can be found in northeastern part; near Monticello, a person would see corn growing; near Ft. Wayne, a person would see dairy farms.

95. 0–500 feet above sea level; higher; students should indicate that they checked the color of the land near Lake Erie and compared it to the elevation scale.

96. Barbados

97. Students' paragraphs should include the following information: the battle at Camden took place in South Carolina; the battle at Saratoga was fought in 1777; battles took place in 1775 in Massachusetts and New York.

98. Atlanta, Georgia is closer to Knoxville, Tennessee. Atlanta is about 150 miles from Knoxville, Tennessee, Raleigh, North Carolina is over 300 miles from Knoxville. You might suggest students use a ruler or map scale strip when determining distances.

99. Appalachian Mountain; Piedmont; Allegheny Mountains; 6,684 feet

100. Canada, the United States, Mexico

101. Ohio, Indiana, Illinois, Wisconsin, Michigan; Spain; Great Britain

102. southeast, southwest, northwest

103. The first and fourth sentences are true. The other sentences

McGraw-Hill School Division

can be rewritten as follows: Tennessee is in the Southeast; Oregon is in the West.

104. Southern Hemisphere; to check the accuracy of their clues, you may want to have students read their clues aloud and find one another's mystery hemispheres.

105. Lancaster. Lancaster is about 60 miles from Philadelphia. Pottstown is about 30 miles from Philadelphia. You might suggest students use a ruler or map scale strip when determining distances.

106. Students' paragraphs should include the following information: the Lewis and Clark Expedition began and ended in St. Louis; the expedition crossed the Rocky Mountains; the expedition traveled through the Louisiana Purchase area and the Oregon Country.

107. Southwest; about 600 miles; 150 miles to Tulsa, Oklahoma.

108. Southeast from Puerto Rico to St. Lucia; south from St. Lucia to Trinidad.

109. Tallahassee, Florida; Raleigh, North Carolina; Montgomery, Alabama; Richmond, Virginia.

110. Provo, Utah

111. West; Northeast; Middle West.

112. Ottawa is the national capital of Canada; Washington, D.C., is the national capital of the United States; Mexico City is the national capital of Mexico.

113. Oregon Trail; Ft. Bridger; Independence Rock, Red Buttes, Split Rock, South Pass

114. Virginia, Tennessee, Arkansas; Texas

115. The first and third sentences are true. The other sentence can be rewritten as follows: the elevation map shows the height above sea level of the Columbia Plateau.

116. Southeast; northeast

117. is south of Illinois—Louisiana; is crossed by 90°W latitude—Wisconsin, Louisiana; is north of 40°N latitude—Wisconsin

118. 40°N latitude, 100°W longitude: United States; 40°N latitude, 140°E longitude: Japan; 20°S latitude, 20°E longitude: Namibia; 0° latitude, 20°E longitude: Congo

119. From Peoria, Illinois, the friend would travel about 300 miles to Frankfort, Kentucky. She would pass through Indiana. She would travel 600 miles from Frankfort to Newark, New Jersey. She would pass through Ohio, West Virginia, Maryland, and Pennsylvania.

120. Johnstown

121. Santa Fe, New Mexico, to Phoenix, Arizona. The distance from Santa Fe to Phoenix is about 375 miles. The distance from Santa Fe to Austin, Texas, is about 600 miles. You might suggest students use a ruler or map scale strip when determining distances.

122. Utah, Illinois

123. The first, second, and fourth sentences can be answered using the map key.

124. Students' fact sheets should include the following information: the Francis Marion National Forest is located in South Carolina; Jamestown is north; there are two ranger stations south; the national forest has two ranger stations.

125. Reno, Nevada is not a state capital; Madison, Wisconsin is a state capital; Memphis, Tennessee is not a state capital; Des Moines, Iowa is a state capital.

126. The Fall Line Road; Memphis.

127. Southeast; 150 miles; southwest.

128. All of the sentences are false and can be rewritten as follows: Donner Pass was located along the California Trail; Whitman's Mission was located near Ft. Walla Walla; the Old Spanish Trail led to Los Angeles; Ft. Laramie was located near Castle Rock and Chimney Rock.

129. Facts learned from the political map might include some of the following: New Mexico borders Arizona, Colorado, Oklahoma, and Texas; Santa Fe is the capital of New Mexico; Albuquerque is located along the Rio Grande. Facts learned from the physical map might include some of the following: the Pecos River flows from north to south in New Mexico; Wheeler Peak is 13,065 feet high; much of New Mexico is mountainous.

130. Rosario, Argentina: 30°S latitude, 60°W longitude; Houston, Texas: 30°N latitude, 90°W longitude; Nuuk, Greenland: 60°N latitude, 60°W longitude

131. Reno, Nevada: 40°N latitude, 120°W longitude; Jacksonville, Florida: 30°N latitude, 80°W longitude; Honolulu, Hawaii: 20°N latitude, 160°W longitude

132. St. Louis, Missouri; New Orleans, Louisiana; Charlotte, North Carolina

133. New Orleans, Louisiana; 30°N latitude, 90°W longitude

134. Kansas, Pennsylvania, North Carolina, New Mexico

135. Eastern Hemisphere; to check the accuracy of their clues, you may want to have students read their clues aloud and find one another's mystery hemispheres.

136. Manaus, Brazil, and Portland, Oregon are farthest apart.

137. About 300 miles long; shorter; longer

138. Seattle, Washington; Pocatello, Idaho; Casper, Wyoming

139. Japan; to check the accuracy of their clues, you may want to have students read their clues aloud and find one another's mystery countries.

140. Cities the group might pass include: Omaha, Nebraska; Kansas City, Kansas; Kansas City, Missouri; Jefferson City, Missouri; St. Louis, Missouri. Landforms the group might see include plains and hills.

141. Mesabi Range; to check the accuracy of their clues, you may want to have students read their clues aloud and solve one another's riddles.

142. France, Germany, Poland

143. Students' paragraphs should include the following information: the Wasatch Range; the Columbia Plateau is north of the Great Basin; the Mojave and Sonora deserts are south of the Great Basin.

144. Albany, New York; Burlington is about 150 miles from Albany, New York about 300 miles from Buffalo, New York. You might suggest students use a ruler or map scale strip when determining distances.

145. Myanmar, Bangladesh, India, Pakistan, Indian Ocean, Oman, United Arab Emirates, Saudi Arabia, Egypt, Libya, Algeria, Mali, Mauritauia, Morocco, Atlantic Ocean, The Bahamas, Cuba, Gulf of Mexico, Mexico, Pacific Ocean, Taiwan, China

146. Denmark, Germany, Poland, Russia, Lithuania, Latvia, Estonia, Finland, Sweden

147. Little Rock, Arkansas; to check the accuracy of their clues, you may want to have students read their clues aloud and find one another's mystery cities.

148. Students' fact sheets should include the following information: Mexico is located in the North American Continent. It borders the southwest United States. Its capital city is Mexico City; Mexico has the Sierra Madre Oriental and Sierra Madre Occidental mountain ranges.

149. Students' fact sheets should include the following information: Egypt is located between 20°N latitude and 40°N latitude, and 20°E longitude and 40°E longitude; countries that border Egypt include Libya, Sudan, and Israel.

150. India